# How To
# Change *the*
# Lightbulbs
# When I'm Gone

D1496124

# How To
# Change *the*
# Lightbulbs
# When I'm Gone

---

*A Book About After*

ROBYN SECHLER

# Contents

# PREFACE

When I began working on this book, my father had been gone for 10 years. This book had been in the back of my mind since the time he passed away, and I haven't been able to stop thinking about how valuable it can be. I can't take full credit for its contents, because he left behind a similar book for my family to have as a resource. My father titled his version "Upon My Demise".

I opted for a little less grim of a title but the ideas are the same! My family still reads that book, to this day, to find the answers to the questions that would otherwise go unanswered. These include not only where the lightbulbs are, but also how to change those ones that are no so easy to change!

# INTRODUCTION

This book is designed for you to leave answers to the questions your loved ones may have after you pass, become incapacitated, or otherwise unable to share the information with them yourself.

You may not have answers to every question in this booklet, and likewise, you may have answers to questions we have not asked.

Use this book to brainstorm about the important ones.

CHAPTER ONE

# What Do You Want Your Loved Ones To Know?

Talking about what happens "after" is not always an easy topic. Most people are not sitting around the dinner table asking one another what they want their funeral to look like, but that doesn't make it any less important! Everyone's wishes and desires are different, and it is so important that your loved ones know how to honor yours. Take a moment to consider the following questions and write in the answers on the following pages.

**Have you already made funeral arrangements?**

_____

_____

_____

_____

**If so, please provide that information including location and contact person.**

_____

_____

_____

_____

**Do you wish to be buried? Cremated?**

_____

_____

_____

_____

**What clothes do you wish to be buried in?**

_____

_____

_____

_____

**Who should be invited?**

_____

_____

_____

_____

**Do you wish a religious official?**

_____

_____

_____

**Do you wish flowers?**

_____

_____

_____

**Do you wish music?**

_____

_____

_____

**Do you have a location?**

_____

_____

_____

_____

CHAPTER TWO

# Important Contacts

One of the first questions that comes up when someone you love passes away is "who should I call?" Don't leave your family searching for the phone numbers of important contacts. Place them right here, in one place where they can always find them.

WHO
DO I
CALL

## Physician

Name:_____

_____

Phone Number:_____

Location:_____

_____


## Attorney:

Name:_____

_____

Phone Number:_____

Location:_____

_____


## Financial Advisor

Name:_____

_____

Phone Number:_____

Location:_____

_____

## Accountant

Name:_____

_____

Phone Number:_____

Location:_____

_____

## Bank

Name:_____

_____

Phone Number:_____

Location:_____

_____

## Family Members:

Name:_____

Phone Number:_____

Name:_____

Phone Number:_____

Name:_____

Phone Number:_____

CHAPTER THREE

# Digital Assets

Cell phones and computers have become a hub for so much information over the past decade including photos, videos, apps, downloads, records and more. The items trapped in your phone and computer, as well as those housed in various clouds, are what we refer to as "digital assets". Let your loved ones know where your digital assets are stored and how they can access them. Don't let your photos be lost, after all they are a legacy for you to leave behind.

**Where are your photos and videos stored?**

Snapfish

Amazon

Google Photo

FOREVER.com

Twitter

Facebook

LinkedIn

**Write down all the places you store your digital assets so your loved ones can view your photos or gather any files they might need.**

_____

_____

_____

_____

_____

_____

_____

_____

_____

_____

_____

_____

_____

_____

_____

_____

_____

_____

_____

_____

_____

How to Change the Light bulbs when I'm Gone

_____

_____

_____

_____

_____

_____

_____

_____

_____

_____

_____

_____

_____

_____

_____

_____

_____

_____

_____

_____

_____

_____

_____

_____

CHAPTER FOUR

# Subscriptions and Memberships

**C**onsider the subscriptions you have set up for yourself over the past 5 years, or so. Are they ongoing? Will they automatically renew unless you tell them otherwise? What about your medications? This may be helpful to do on an ongoing basis rather than trying to remember them all, when you sign up for something be sure to come back to this page and add it in!

Medications

Magazines

Amazon Prime

Health Insurance

Gym Membership

Nexflix

Audible

Spotify

Disney Plus

**What subscriptions do you have, and what should your loved ones do with those when you pass?"**

CHAPTER FIVE

# Where is Your...

There are so many important documents that get collected over the years. Most people have several storage places that is only loosely organized, if at all. There is nothing worse than searching for something you know exists but cannot be found! Help your loved ones by telling them exactly where these documents are so they can find them easily and quickly.

## Birth Certificate

_____

_____

_____

## Social Security Card

_____

_____

_____

## Marriage Certificate

_____

_____

_____

## Military Discharge Papers

_____

_____

_____

## Car Title

_____

_____

**Deed to Your Home**

**Power of Attorney**

**Computer**

**Hard Drive**

## Will/Trust/Legal Documents

_____

_____

_____

_____

## Insurance Policy

_____

_____

_____

_____

## Citizenship Card

_____

_____

_____

_____

## Divorce/Annulment Papers

_____

_____

_____

_____

## Prenuptial Agreements

_____

_____

_____

_____

## Death Certificates of Other Family Members

_____

_____

_____

_____

## Passport

_____

_____

_____

_____

## Organ Donation Papers_

_____

_____

_____

_____

## Real Estate Deeds

_____

_____

_____

_____

## Mortgage Statements

_____

_____

_____

_____

## List of Valuables

_____

_____

_____

_____

## Safety Deposit Box Information

_____

_____

_____

_____

CHAPTER SIX

# In the Home

**What needs to be done for the house in the winter**

**What needs to be done for the house in the summer**

**Where are the lightbulbs stored and which lights to they belong to**

_____

_____

_____

_____

**How do I turn on/off the water**

_____

_____

_____

_____

**How do I turn on/off the gas**

_____

_____

_____

_____

## Who to call if there is a problem

_____

_____

_____

_____

## Where are warranty

_____

_____

_____

_____

CHAPTER SEVEN

# Home Utillities

It takes a village to run a home. Provide the names, phone numbers and other pertinent information for each utility company that you use.

## Gas Company

Name:_____

_____

Phone Number:_____

Location:_____

_____

Account Number: _____

## Water Company

Name:_____

_____

Phone Number:_____

Location:_____

_____

Account Number: _____

## Electric Company

Name:_____

_____

Phone Number:_____

Location:_____

_____

Account Number: _____

## Sewage Company

Name:_____

_____

Phone Number:_____

Location:_____

_____

Account Number:_____

## Trash Company

Name:_____

_____

Phone Number:_____

Location:_____

_____

Account Number:_____

## Cable/Internet

Name:_____

_____

Phone Number:_____

Location:_____

_____

Account Number:_____

## Cell Phone

Name:_____

_____

Phone Number:_____

Location:_____

_____

Account Number: _____

## Snow Removal

Name:_____

_____

Phone Number:_____

Location:_____

_____

Account Number: _____

## Lawn Care

Name:_____

_____

Phone Number:_____

Location:_____

_____

Account Number: _____

## Credit Cards

Name:_____

_____

Phone Number:_____

Location:_____

_____

Account Number: _____

## Home Security System

Name:_____

_____

Phone Number:_____

Location:_____

_____

Account Number: _____

## Post Office Box _____

Name:_____

_____

Phone Number:_____

Location:_____

_____

Account Number: _____

## Car Payment

Name:_____

_____

Phone Number:_____

Location:_____

_____

Account Number:_____

## Taxes

Name:_____

_____

Phone Number:_____

Location:_____

_____

Account Number:_____

Include name, account numbers, phone numbers

CHAPTER EIGHT

# Finances

Finances can be extremely stressful to manage after the loss of a loved one. Easing that burden, if even just a little bit, is hugely helpful. Include names, phone numbers and other pertinent information in regards to the following topics.

**What financial institutions do you use?**

_____

_____

_____

_____

**Do you have an IRA? If so, where?**

_____

_____

_____

_____

**What credit cards do you carry?**

_____

_____

_____

_____

**Do you have any outstanding IOU's?**

_____

_____

_____

_____

**Do you owe any taxes?**

_____
_____
_____
_____

**What bank is your mortgage through?**

_____
_____
_____
_____

**Do you have a life insurance policy?**

_____
_____
_____
_____

**Where are your bank statements?**

_____
_____
_____
_____

**Do you have any Payable on Death accounts?**

_____

_____

_____

_____

**Do you own any Stocks and Bonds? If so, what for?**

_____

_____

_____

_____

**Where are your past tax returns stored?**

_____

_____

_____

_____

**Do you have a life insurance policy?**

_____

_____

_____

_____

**Where are your bank statements?**

_____

_____

_____

_____

**Do you have a 401K?**

_____

_____

_____

_____

**Do you have a Pension?**

_____

_____

_____

_____

**Do you have a home-owners policy?**

_____

_____

_____

_____

CHAPTER NINE

# Family Pets

**D**on't forget about the little guys! Well, depending on the type of animals you have, they may or may not be so little! Leave some directions behind so your human loved ones can take care of your furry loved ones.

What pets do you have?

What type of care do they each require?

Who is their vet?

What type of food do they eat?

Do they have any special needs?

CHAPTER TEN

# Online Accounts

**T**hough many people share passwords to online accounts, you should be very careful about doing so. Password sharing can be risky and may be a violation of your contract with particular companies. You should consider handling account access through estate planning documents like your Last Will & Testament.

List your Online accounts below.

**What online accounts do you have?**

Email

Access to Photos and Videos

Online Banking

Retail Stores

Social Media

Cell Phone Service